104Challenges

Become the Best You

Tad Mitchell

FOREWORD BY
Stella
Grizont

Thank you to the WellRight team who served as guinea pigs testing the challenges. Thank you to Renee and Tricia, our editors. Thank you to our reviewers. Thank you to Tamara who refined the artwork and did the layout. Thank you to my brainstorming buddy, Alisa. Thank you to all who provided feedback.

Tad

Disclaimer: Information in *104 Challenges* is for educational purposes only and is not meant to substitute for the advice of a medical professional. You should consult with a health care professional before starting any diet, exercise, or supplementation program.

First Edition

Printed in U.S.A.

ISBN 978-0-9964417-9-7

More information about the book can be found at www.104Challenges.com.

Reviewers

Medical

David Mitchell, MD, PhD

Nutrition

Kristen Balchan, RD, LDN

Exercise

Michael Grimsley, MPH, CHES, CSCS

Psychology

Christian Laplante, PhD, R PSYCH, MFT

Financial

Cherrish Holland, Certified Credit Counselor
Brian Ramaker, Certified Financial Advisor, AAMS®

Foreword

Stella Grizont, MAPP
Executive Coach and Speaker
Creator of Work Happier Now

We all want to thrive and, actually, we all know how to do it. The problem is resistance. We don't always feel like doing what we need to do, or maybe we don't believe it's possible. For me, while I have great intentions, sometimes I don't know where to start nor do I always have the energy to figure it out. Sometimes I get tired or distracted. Maybe I just procrastinate. I have wonderfully creative ways of avoiding the very thing I want so badly—my own transformation to be better. Can you relate?

By the way, it's my job to help other people work happier and live better. Companies hire me to engage their employees. I've coached more than 1,600 leaders in 27 countries, and I have a Master's in Applied Positive Psychology (aka, the science of happiness and well-being) from the University of Pennsylvania. Yet, I STILL get stuck, myself.

The reason this happens is because we all need something or someone to help us with what's inside. Enter *104 Challenges*. I LOVE these brilliantly designed, bite-size ways to grow. Tad Mitchell makes the ability for people to become "more well" not only doable but fun! As I read through the challenges, I found myself being inspired, filled with an exciting sense of possibility.

When it comes down to it, the key to truly flourishing is knowing that you have the power to create your own reality, no matter what. When you see yourself making progress on what matters, by doing these challenges, you actually develop an organic sense of confidence. Tad Mitchell sets up his readers for success by inviting them to choose their own adventure and then conquer it! Whether you complete one challenge or many, simply doing what's on the page will give you a glimpse at how powerful, brave, and beautiful you are.

Here's to your flourishing!

Introduction

Tad Mitchell, MBA
President and CEO, WellRight

I've spent my entire career developing software, usually software that I don't use. In the early days of WellRight, I saw it as great fun because I viewed it as another software development project. At some point early on, I caught the wellness bug. I started eating better and lost 25 pounds. I read *The Power of Habit* by Charles Duhigg and became a habit groupie—so much so that I wrote my own book, *21 Habits: A Wellness Survival Guide* with my friend Michael Guercio.

As I created one new habit after another, it felt as if my life or personal progression had accelerated. In fact, at my new rate of change, it almost felt like I had been standing still for the first 50 years of my life. As I continued my journey, I started focusing on all dimensions of my life (purpose, emotional, social, occupational, financial) and not just the physical. Wellness expanded to overall well-being. I realized that being out of balance in one area had greatly impacted the other areas of my life.

I was becoming better, felt empowered, and believed I could become whatever I wanted. I was making tremendous progress, but it felt hollow because becoming what *I* wanted felt wrong. Was self-actualization achieved by focusing on yourself? My heart said *no*.

If not my plan, then whose plan was I to follow? Clearly the same source that told me that it wasn't about what I wanted. Books have been written about accessing this source, but I think it can be simpler than we make it out to be. One day I felt it was time for me to move on to my next challenge. I simply asked what I should work on next. Boom! The answer came. I didn't use my mind or some software program to logically deduce what my ideal next step would be. I submitted to the Universe and asked for direction—resulting in a direction I would not have come up with on my own.

This concept—submitting to the Universe to find direction—is the first concept most publications on habits lack. Another overlooked concept is submitting to the Universe for strength. Just as I asked for direction, I can ask for strength: "It was your idea to work on this, so please help me out. Clear my mind. Give me hope. Change my heart. Make me strong."

Give it a try and accelerate your personal progress. It will be exhilarating, like taking off in an airplane for the first time. Sure, it can be scary or even painful, but the feeling of exhilaration will be worth it!

Challenges

Coming**Soon**

Anticipate today

Coffee with
Addison
@ 10:15am

The Coming Soon Challenge invites you to write something down you're anticipating in the next 24 hours, each morning (or evening) for the next 30 days. If you don't have anything you're looking forward to, adjust your schedule a bit and plan to do something you will enjoy. Ask a friend to meet up for coffee. Choose to eat one of your favorite meals for dinner. Set aside time to work on a project or hobby you really enjoy. Think of something during your work day you enjoy, like working with a certain person or doing a certain type of work. Your anticipation will be more fun and much greater if you make your plan a few days or even weeks in advance.

Simply anticipating something you're looking forward to can be just as satisfying as actually experiencing it. So why not anticipate many good things in your life? This way you get to enjoy them *twice*—once in anticipation and again when you actually have the experience! Having something to look forward to makes life more enjoyable. It's simple: look ahead, anticipate, and then enjoy!

Due|It

Do something you've been putting off

The Due It Challenge invites you to do something that you've been putting off. Life goes by so quickly. We push onward, trying to keep up with our daily activities, and pretty soon a year has passed, then two, then 10—without getting anything big done. Once you decide to do something, no matter what, somehow you find time for it. This challenge is your opportunity to pick something important that you'd like to accomplish and get it done. It can be something small or big, but the more you desire to accomplish it, the more satisfying it will be.

This challenge isn't one to push you to do more as much as it is a challenge to have you try to do what's most important. List those things you would like to do that are important. Your natural tendency will be to pick an important item that is urgent, but instead pick an important item that is *not* urgent. These high-importance/low-urgency items tend to have the biggest impact in our lives and in the lives of others. So pick one and get it done! Not only will it make you feel good, it will give you the confidence to tackle another, similar item. Life's too short—DUE IT!

Focus5

Identify your top priorities

The Focus 5 Challenge invites you to list the top 25 things you want to do—and then reduce the list to only five. Dreaming up your big list of all 25 is vital to this challenge, even if they might seem a bit crazy (or boring) as you write them down. You can include anything that you're currently working on or that is a priority in your life already. Once you have your list of 25, review it thoroughly and cross off 20 things. Keep the five items that you want to accomplish the most. Write those down on a new page and post it where you can read them often.

Perhaps as interesting as the five items you kept on your list are the 20 items you crossed off. We often spread ourselves thin, trying to accomplish too many things at once, but not necessarily being productive or successful with any of them. See if you can let go of the 20 items and not invest any time in them until your first five are complete. If you keep wanting to prioritize something that's not on your Focus 5, consider changing your list so you have a new top 5. Don't worry. You can always work on something else after you complete your top items. Give it a try and see how much you get done!

Purpose

MissionReady

Read your mission statement out loud

My Mission Statement

The Mission Ready Challenge invites you to say your mission statement out loud each day. Of course, you'll first need a mission statement in order to do this challenge. (See the Mission Possible Challenge in *102 Challenges: Become the Best You* to help write yours). Post your mission statement where you'll see it every day—like on your bathroom mirror or on your desk. When you first see it each day, read it out loud (even if it feels awkward). The earlier you read it each day, the better. It will be one of your first accomplishments of the day!

Vocalizing your mission statement every day will remind you of your purpose. If you no longer like your self-defined purpose after a few days, it's okay to change it. It's natural to update your mission statement over time. Hearing yourself speak your mission statement aloud will help it sink into your heart and mind and become a part of who you are. Hopefully the words will resonate in your mind as you go about your daily business, reminding you why you do what you do, and maybe even changing what you do!

Mount**Rushmore**
Write about 4 people you respect

The Mount Rushmore Challenge invites you to write about the four most influential people in your life. Write about each person, stating why you respect them and what attributes they have that you'd like to have. Include stories or experiences that illustrate your points. Write as much as you'd like. You don't need to share what you have written with the people you write about, but if you did, it would certainly brighten their day!

Taking the time to list what we admire about others can inspire us to grow in meaningful ways. Even selecting our heroes in the first place can help us recognize what speaks to us and what we want to accomplish in life. Don't get discouraged if your specific strengths or talents differ from the person you admire. You can still be motivated by their greatness even with varied interests, talents, or personality traits. The point is to better understand what you'd like to become. Once you recognize that, the easier it will be to become who you want to be.

PrayerList

Write down what you are praying for

Purpose

Emotional

Social

The Prayer List Challenge invites you to compile a list of things you'd like to pray for—and use it as you pray for the next 30 days. List things you are grateful for; things you'd like to change or make right; people and their specific needs, situations that are troubling you; and areas in your life where you need additional strength, support, or comfort. You could even pray to be inspired with ideas of things that you should add to your prayer list. The idea is not to write a prayer word for word, but to create a list of prompts that you can use while you pray. Consider posting the list on the wall where you pray or keeping it in a journal you can open while you pray.

Writing down your prayer list can help you be more focused in your prayers. It can also help you remember what's important to you and who is in need, possibly giving you ideas on how you can help. Keeping a record of your prayers will also allow you to look back at what you prayed about and notice any blessings that came as a result. You can also contemplate how each prayer was answered. Even if the answer is not what you'd hoped for, you can pray for understanding. Give a prayer list a try and see if it doesn't enhance your prayers!

Top 100

Set 100 life goals

The Top 100 Challenge invites you to make a list of 100 things you would like to accomplish before you die. One hundred goals may seem overwhelming, but listing that many will require you to expand your thinking beyond the typical. You will explore parts of your life that you normally wouldn't consider while setting goals. It will also help you realize that you have many things you'd like to accomplish—and help you figure out which ones you'd like to start with.

As you create your list of 100 goals, you'll go beyond big lifetime goals to listing smaller bite-size goals. Smaller goals are more achievable and you'll be able to complete them more quickly. As you conquer these smaller goals, the satisfaction you feel with each success will propel you to achieve some of your more ambitious goals. Who knows? By simply listing your goals, you may end up accomplishing two or three times as many as you would have otherwise. Where will your goals take you?

Top**Priority**

Create a daily to-do list

The Top Priority Challenge invites you to create a to-do list each morning and use it throughout the day. Write down everything you want to get done for the day—if you prioritize the things on your list, that's even better! You might not finish everything on your list, but you can use what's left as a starting point for the following day. You'll love that satisfying feeling of crossing off tasks one by one and getting so much done!

Using a to-do list each day is a simple way to be more productive. It can help you focus your efforts on the important things you need to get done. It may even drive you to work a little harder or a little longer because you'll have a clear target. However, be careful that your to-do list doesn't begin to rule your life. You can be flexible with it if other things come up and your priorities need to change. Be mindful that a to-do list is a tool, not your master. Use it to that end and it can help you organize and better enjoy your entire day.

5Stars

Praise 3 local businesses online

Emotional

The 5 Stars Challenge invites you to write a positive post online for three local businesses. Just do a search for a business that you like and find a link or a window to give a rating or review. Be specific about what you like about them. Give them an excellent star rating and consider taking a photo and adding it, too. Not only will you be helping out the business you review, you'll be helping all those patrons who are curious about it!

Many of us tend not to say anything about a business or a shopping experience unless we've encountered a problem. This behavior may be natural, but it's not necessarily healthy for us or for the world. As you focus more on the good interactions and transactions you've had, your negative experiences with other businesses will fade from your attention. You'll feel better inside while you also generate positive energy outward.

Accept It

Let go of what annoys you

Emotional

Social

The Accept It Challenge invites you to write down something about someone who annoys you and decide to let that thing go—do this each day for 30 days. Write down the name of the person and what annoys you. Then pause for a moment and tell yourself to overlook whatever that is—and instead focus on the good qualities in that person. If there are many things that annoy you in a single day, make multiple entries that day, but be sure to make at least one entry each day. You'll be surprised how this gets harder to do toward the end of the month because you will become more patient and tolerant through this process! At the end of this challenge, you may want to destroy your list as a symbol that you have moved on.

We create our own reality with our thoughts and reactions. If that reality is filled with what we dislike about those around us, we end up living in a very negative place. The good news is that YOU have the power to turn this around—not by changing others who annoy you, but by changing your response. As you choose to overlook or ignore shortcomings, they will eventually vanish from your radar. This challenge will help you consciously dismiss the annoyances in your life—and make room for a more positive, pleasant life.

Bad**Memory**

Journal something you want to forget

Emotional

The Bad Memory Challenge invites you to write about one experience that you would like to forget. Think of something that keeps returning to your mind year after year but is something that you'd rather forget. Take some time to write down every detail of that experience, including your thoughts, impressions, and feelings. Don't rush it. You could start with a rough draft and revisit it a few days later. Add to it until you feel it's complete, or if you'd just like to write it out once and be done with it, that's fine, too. Once you've finished, you could file it away, burn it, or even put it in the shredder to symbolize letting go.

This challenge is similar to writing down something important that is stuck in your mind when you're trying to fall asleep. Once you write it down, your mind can let go of that thought. That same freedom can come to your mind and your emotional state when you have a recurring memory that you'd like to forget. Writing down the experience will help release it from your memory, free your mind, and make your life more pleasant.

CandleLight
Burn candles

Emotional

The Candle Light Challenge invites you to burn candles each day for 30 days. You can burn a single candle or various arrangements of candles at any time of the day. Winter is an excellent season to enjoy candles with the early nightfall and cooler weather. A scented candle can bring you further enjoyment, but unscented candles can still bring calmness to your environment. If you forget one day, burn the candles a little longer the next day. Place the candles well within sight so you can feel that sense of relaxation and also ensure the candles are burning safely. Remember to blow them out before you leave home!

There's something relaxing and soothing about the gentle flicker of a flame. For most of the earth's history, fire was a part of daily life. Now with modern technology, we may go months without ever seeing a flame. Our central heating and electric lighting are certainly more convenient and safer, but they don't come close to providing the comforting feeling of a flame flickering off in the distance. Try reading a book by candlelight like people used to long ago. Enjoy a long bath or eat dinner by candlelight. Don't forget to watch the ethereal plume of smoke when you blow out your candle—allowing your stress to dissipate in a similar way.

The Do Over Challenge invites you to ponder your day, then write down at least one thing you wish you had done differently—noting specifically *what* you should have done instead—for the next 30 days. You can evaluate your day later that evening or the next morning (before you start a new day). You don't have to write a novel, but some days may require more thought and analysis than others. The more you think through the scenario, the greater the impact it will have on you.

As the phrase, "Hindsight is 20/20," attests, we all do things we wish we had done differently. It's part of our nature. We are imperfect beings and learn from our mistakes. The ability to change and improve is an amazing component of the human experience. This challenge can help you pinpoint where and how you need to change so you can be the person you want to be. Set aside time for introspective thinking; it's the seed of meaningful change.

ExcuseYou

No blaming

Emotional

The Excuse You Challenge invites you to stop blaming others for the next 30 days. The first step is to recognize when you start to blame someone. Often it takes the form of explaining to yourself or to others why you are frustrated, upset, late, unhappy, or some other negative consequence. Ideally, you'll catch yourself before you speak your thought aloud, but if you do slip, then do your best to undo what you've said. Over the course of the challenge, you'll get better at it. Eventually, you'll stop blaming people in your mind too, and feel a sense of liberation knowing that you are in control, not just an object acted upon by others.

Feeling resentful toward others can affect your physical health as well as your emotional outlook. Anger and bitterness have been scientifically associated with high blood pressure, heart disease, headaches, fatigue, and elevated stress. Living in a state of blame doesn't bring happiness. It may seem like saying that someone else is wrong and you are right will make you feel better, but it just leaves you feeling frustrated with the injustice of it all. Instead, recognize that you can't change other people. Love others even with their imperfections and stay away from those who bring you harm. Don't play the blame game.

Go**Fetch**

Play with your pet 20 times

The Go Fetch Challenge invites you to play with your pet 20 times in the next 30 days. Play fetch with your dog. Snuggle up with your bunny. Drag a string across the floor for your cat to chase. Hold your guinea pig and watch it scamper around. The goal is to set aside some time to spend with your pet—without your usual distractions—and simply enjoy your time together. If you don't have a pet, offer to walk a neighbor's dog, feed a friend's cat, or just spend some time observing birds, squirrels, or even bugs you see out in nature.

Animals can certainly benefit from human attention and interaction, but did you know there are perks for you, as well? Physical touch with a pet can produce oxytocin in your body—which can make you feel relaxed, reduce stress, and even lower your blood pressure and heart rate. Taking your dog for a walk or a trail run will give you the added benefits of getting outside. Even simply pausing to watch ants busily working or bees buzzing about on the lawn can get your mind away from its usual mode and give it some much needed rest. If you'd rather cuddle with your pet instead of play, that's completely fine!

Inspire Me
Learn from others

Emotional

Social

The Inspire Me Challenge invites you to write down one thing someone did that day that inspired you each day for 30 days. It could be anything—how they responded in a tough situation, the way they made you and everyone around them feel important, or how patient they were—that makes you reflect and want to be better. Some of the most inspiring actions will be done by complete strangers you encounter. Feel free to tell the other person how they inspired you (although that's not part of the challenge). If you forget a day, write down two things the next day.

When we look for the good in others, it's amazing how much there is to find. This challenge takes this search to the next level—to look for good things that truly inspire you. In addition to being inspired, you'll feel a deeper connection with these individuals and the world in general. Life will become less mundane and your burdens will feel lighter. Others will have a greater impact on you—an impact so big that it motivates you to improve your life! What will you learn from the people you encounter in your life?

IChoose

Never say "I have to"

The I Choose Challenge invites you to refrain from saying, "I have to" and replace it with "I get to." Saying "I get to go to work tomorrow" is not only more positive, it's also more truthful. You don't *have* to go to work—you *choose* to go to work. You control what you do each day. Realizing that you "get to" do something can help you view the situation with more positivity and gratitude. If you catch yourself saying "I have to" during this challenge, no worries; just say it again with, "I get to."

A bit of shifting in your thinking can broaden your perspective. When you take a look around, you realize that not everyone gets to do what you do, whether it's because of health issues, opportunities, or where they live in the world. Even just looking back at times you've been sick or injured can help you recognize that being able to do what you do each day is a gift. This simple change in perspective from "I have to" to "I get to" will help you enjoy your life more!

CHALLENGE
18

LoveMachine
Project love

Emotional

Social

The Love Machine Challenge invites you to spend five minutes or more each day projecting love for the next 30 days. To project love, spend time thinking about (or even writing about) those in your life who you are grateful for—pondering the specific reasons you have love for them and the specific ways they've shown love to you. Once you've had some success pondering those you love, try pondering those in your life who might be a little harder to love. You also may want to try projecting love while you're in the presence of the receiving person. The outcomes may surprise you!

Projecting love is less demonstrative than expressing love, but it can be just as powerful. When you think about people you love and contemplate the reasons why you love them, you will project that energy in ways that will be uplifting to others. Yes, believe it or not, when we have positive, loving feelings inside, others can sense that and will feel good inside, as well. It will certainly impact you for good, too! There is great power in projecting love. Start sharing your love today!

EnjoyLife
Do something you enjoy

Emotional

The Enjoy Life Challenge invites you to do something you enjoy each day for the next 30 days. First, pinpoint what you truly enjoy doing: going for a run, reading the paper with your coffee, watching a show, playing video games, reading a good book, or playing the guitar. Then, choose a time in your day to make that happen. The amount of time you spend doing what you enjoy is up to you. Set yourself up for success by setting a very small goal—five minutes or even one minute! If you end up spending more time at it, great!

In today's busy world, it's easy to get caught up in an endless barrage of things you *need* to do. If you don't spend any time doing what you *like* to do, you may start to feel like your life is drudgery and you will get burned out. Doing something you enjoy each day will give you something to look forward to and will help you feel refreshed and regenerated. Make sure to mix it up and add variety to what you do throughout the challenge. Take note of what is the most fulfilling, most relaxing, and most recharging—each may serve a different purpose. What do you enjoy doing?

No**Snoozing**

Don't press snooze on your alarm clock

Emotional

Physical

Occupational

The No Snoozing Challenge invites you to get up right away when your alarm clock rings instead of pressing the snooze button or lingering longer in bed. If you know you need to sleep longer, set your alarm for later—and then get up right away when it rings. Decide at the beginning of this challenge that you'll get up as soon as your alarm goes off every single day. It will be much easier to succeed when you've already made the commitment rather than debating it each morning when you're sleepy. Try placing your alarm clock across the room where you cannot reach it. Before you know it, you'll be in a new pattern of getting up promptly.

We've all heard the phrase, "You snooze, you lose." Getting up immediately when your alarm clock rings means that you've started your day with success! You've already kept a commitment with yourself. What a great way to start the day! As you keep your personal commitments, you will become stronger and capable of doing more. It's so simple, yet so powerful. Try getting up right away each day and see if you like it.

Rock Star

Sing daily

Emotional

The Rock Star Challenge invites you to sing for five minutes or more every day over the next 30 days. You can sing in the shower, in the car, as you walk to work, or during your work-out. Sing your favorite song over and over if you'd like. It doesn't matter how good you sound, just sing! If you miss a day, no worries—just sing for twice as long the next day.

Whether you're happy or sad, singing out loud will fill your soul. Singing is a natural antidepressant—it will boost your mood and lower your stress level. On top of that, singing will also strengthen your immune system, increase your lung capacity, and brighten your day. As an added benefit, those who are lucky enough to hear your singing will feel happier too—or at least get a good laugh out of it!

SilverLining

Find the good in the bad

Emotional

Social

Occupational

The Silver Lining Challenge invites you to find something good in one negative situation each day for the next 30 days. In other words, when something doesn't go your way, look for the "silver lining." Keep a log. When you encounter misfortune, write it down—then identify how that misfortune could possibly be a good thing. There is no right or wrong assessment. You may never know how or if that negative experience changed your life (or someone else's) for the better, but as you go through this exercise, you will begin to recognize that obstacles may do more than just trip us up or bog us down.

Positive thinking is a great antidote for stress, anxiety, and discouragement. You may have heard the adage, "When life closes a door, it opens a window." While it may be hard at times to find these "windows," everyone can learn to develop the skill of looking at the bright side. Thinking positive thoughts may feel forced or fake at times, but it will have powerful effects that are both physiological and life altering. Start looking for the silver lining and watch yourself become happier and more successful!

Stay**Cation**

Enjoy a local attraction

CHALLENGE
23

Emotional

The Stay Cation Challenge invites you to enjoy a local tourist attraction. It can be a water park, a museum, a concert—any place nearby that sounds fun! Gather ideas online just as if you were going to another city to visit. Don't be afraid to spend some money—act as if you were on vacation somewhere else. You can feel good knowing your money is going back into your own community. Try to visit a place you've never been before or at least somewhere you haven't been in a long time. Bring friends or family along and make it a memorable event.

Many of us travel great distances to visit other places. We make elaborate plans, spend large amounts of money, and try to see as many things as we can in a short amount of time. The funny thing is that other people do the same thing when they visit where we live. The goal of this challenge is to help you enjoy the attractions right in your backyard. You don't need to travel far or pay for lodging and food. You may not even need to take a vacation day. Give a Stay Cation in your own town a try!

WalkingZone

Meditate while you walk

Emotional

Physical

The Walking Zone Challenge invites you to meditate as you walk each day for the next 30 days. Many people think meditation is only done seated in a peaceful place with eyes closed, but there are many ways to meditate. After you begin your trek and find a steady pace, let go of your thoughts and focus on your breath, the sound of your steps, or an object in the distance. As thoughts come to your mind, keep centered on your focal point and let them pass. Once you've gained control of your mind, explore other sensations you are experiencing, like how you feel, and what you see, smell, or hear. Try to do this for five minutes a day. If you go longer, great!

Meditation done while remaining still or with movement is an elixir for your brain. You are allowing your brain to rest when you ignore the chatter of thoughts that constantly bounce around in your mind. You are also training your brain to cut out the "static"—the bombardment of unnecessary thoughts—so you can connect with your inner self, your true self. See what a little meditation each day can do for your well-being. As you learn to meditate while you walk, it will be easy to add meditation to your day without planning extra time for it.

Wire**Less**

Take a break from your phone

Emotional

Social

The Wire Less Challenge invites you to take a one-hour break from your mobile phone each day for the next 30 days. Find a time during the day that you don't necessarily need your phone— then turn it off or leave it behind for at least an hour. If you are concerned that you might miss an important call, set your phone so it only rings for that particular caller and place it far enough away that you won't be tempted to use it, but it's still within earshot. Don't worry. You can do this. You will be just fine without your phone.

Disconnecting from your phone will give you the opportunity to reconnect with yourself and real life. You will be able to focus on what's happening around you and especially on the people who are nearby. You may also find yourself more relaxed while you have a break from texts, emails, and phone calls. Hopefully this challenge will help you feel more comfortable checking your phone less often so you can tune into your real life. Give disconnecting from technology a try and see if it makes life more enjoyable for you!

Worry Wart

Let go of your fears

The Worry Wart Challenge invites you to list one thing you are worried about each day for the next 30 days—and then let go of it. Ask yourself, "What is troubling my mind?" It could be a concern about work, a relationship, money, or a future event—anything that is plaguing your mind. Write it down. Recognize that you have little to no control over the majority of the things you worry about—and let go of the stress you're holding inside. Once you've written your item down, crumple up the paper and throw it in the garbage or run it through a shredder. If an item pops into your head again, that's okay. Write it down again until it stays away!

When you allow your mind to fill with worries, your body absorbs that stress. Worrying takes away any sense of peace, limits your ability to focus properly, and decreases your productivity. Worrying can also interfere with your sleep, appetite, relationships, job performance, and the overall enjoyment of life. This challenge can help! Write down your worries and get them out of your head and out of your life. Don't worry, be happy!

The Back Bite Challenge invites you to not say anything unkind about other people, whether they are present or not, for the next 30 days. As the saying goes, "If you don't have anything nice to say, then don't say anything at all." This is especially important when it comes to people—but it's very hard to do! You may not feel like you're doing very well at this challenge at first. No worries! If you catch yourself saying something negative, say something right away that's positive about the person to redeem yourself. You won't be perfect at this. The important thing is to try each day and eventually you'll break the habit of talking badly about other people.

As you succeed at only saying positive things about others, and stop judging them so harshly, you may let go of being so critical of yourself. By overlooking the bad, the good will become more apparent. Your conversations will become more uplifting. You'll boost up those around you instead of pulling them down. You may even attract more positive friends—and end up spending less time with those who aren't ready for the change. Get ready to experience life in a much more positive way!

BestThing

Help others focus on the positive

The Best Thing Challenge invites you to ask one person a day about a "best thing" for 30 days. Some examples could be "What was the best thing about your weekend?" "What's the best thing about working here?" "What's the best thing about living here?" "What's the best thing that happened today?" Try to ask as many different people as you can, but if you ask the same person more than once during the challenge, that's fine. If you miss a day, catch up by asking two people the next day. Get creative with your questions. You can even find different ways to phrase it, like asking for a number 1 or a favorite thing. The idea is to help others identify and focus on the positive.

Many of us have a habit of talking about the bad things in our lives. It can become a sort of competition to hear a complaint and then try to outdo the other person. The Best Thing Challenge attempts to flip this habit and focus on the good things in our lives. Your simple "best thing" question will cause people to shift gears and start scanning their lives for the good. Think of how powerful this shift could be—you can be the spark that starts it! Be ready with answers to your "best thing" question because someone may turn the question back to you!

Betty**Crocker**

Bake someone a cake

Emotional

Social

The Betty Crocker Challenge invites you to bake a cake or make another homemade treat for someone. You can start by choosing a recipe you love to make or by thinking of a person who needs some cheering up. If you begin with a person in mind, think of a homemade food that person would love to eat. A yummy fruit salad might be just the right thing or maybe a loaf of banana bread. If you have a specialty, make it, then think of someone who would enjoy it. You can attach a heartfelt note for an extra special touch.

Giving gifts is a way to show someone you care about them. Sometimes we don't give a lot of thought to gifts, especially when we can purchase things without much effort. Taking the time to make a gift for someone can be much more meaningful than simply buying something. You will benefit as you ponder the other person while you're cooking, and the recipient will feel honored that you took the time to make something just for them. Who do you know that could use a boost?

Body**Language**
Touch your partner

Social

Physical

The Body Language Challenge invites you to touch your partner in a respectful, loving way at least once a day. Choose a form of physical contact that can be done in public. Give a hug, hold hands, or simply sit close enough that your hips or shoulders touch. Put your hand on their shoulder or give a gentle back rub. The touch doesn't need to be long, but make it significant enough to feel a connection with your partner. You can ask for reciprocation—or just wait and see if that happens naturally. This may be one of the most enjoyable challenges you've tried!

One of the keys to happiness is having at least one deep relationship. One of the deepest relationships you will have is with your partner. Relationships involve an open flow of communication between two people, usually through verbal language. Body language is another great form of communication though, and is especially powerful when it involves touch. A touch can convey feelings and emotions in a way that words can't. Touch your partner throughout the day and see how this connection will help them feel appreciated, valued, and cherished.

Care**Package**

Send a care package

Emotional

Social

The Care Package Challenge invites you to send a care package to someone. Consider sending the package to someone who's away at college or in the military, a sibling or friend, or a young child you may know. If a holiday is coming up, gather items with that holiday theme. Think about what the person would appreciate, maybe something unavailable where they live. Ask others for ideas. Food is usually well received, but don't stop there. Care packages can include a variety of surprises, such as crossword puzzles, a book, or a pair of gloves. Most importantly, include a note in your package.

Like any gift, giving a care package benefits both the giver and the receiver. As you choose the items you'll put in the package, your mind is focused on what the person would like, instead of thinking about yourself. You can take great care in how you wrap everything up, and experience extended joy as you anticipate the arrival of the package and the person's reaction. Help someone feel extra special—start creating your care package today!

D**Compose**
Compost for 30 days

ORGANIC

Emotional

Social

The D Compose Challenge invites you to compost your organic waste for the next 30 days. Most cities have either a bin you can use solely for compost, or they may allow you to fill paper lawn bags with compost for pick-up. To set up for composting in your kitchen, keep an extra trash can or small container by your sink. You can compost plant-based items like fruit and vegetable scraps, coffee grounds and filters, tea bags, and bread. You can compost certain paper items like newspaper and egg cartons as well, but it actually makes more sense to recycle paper—reducing the need to cut down more trees.

Composting can dramatically reduce the amount of trash we put in our landfills, which is helpful for our planet. The process of composting releases fewer harmful gases into the environment than if the organic material were to decompose in a landfill. As an added bonus, the final compost is often available for free to anyone who wants to use it on their lawn and garden. Excess compost can actually be sold for profit. Compost is extremely beneficial for plants because it contains nutrients and microorganisms that promote growth and retain water in the soil. Take the time to compost and do your part to help the planet!

Dinner**Talk**

No phones at dinner

The Dinner Talk Challenge invites you to eat dinner without your phone for the next 30 days. If you're eating with others, explain the challenge and invite them to participate. If you're eating alone, you still can't use your phone. This rule applies even if you receive a phone call. Let it ring like you would if you were in the shower. Better yet, silence your phone before the meal and put it away. With no phone around to distract you, practice your mindfulness skills: savor your food, enjoy your conversation or your solitude, and survey your surroundings.

With all the connectivity and entertainment mobile phones can provide, we have become tethered to them. An occasional break can be healthy—to prove to ourselves that we can exist without a phone, to slow down and enjoy the real world, and to clear our minds from the barrage of endless information. Also, setting our phones aside is the polite thing to do—showing respect for those around us. If nothing else, it's a chance to practice willpower and show the phone and the rest of the world who's really in charge!

EarthBound

Don't brag

Emotional

Social

The Earth Bound Challenge invites you to *not* brag to others about all the good things you do—for the next 30 days. Resist the temptation to ask if everyone liked the dinner you made. Don't share all the things you accomplished on a particular day, how pleased you are with something you did at work, or the weight you just lost. If you'd like to push this challenge a little further, whenever you feel the urge to promote yourself, you could compliment the person you're talking with instead. It is hard to resist talking about yourself, but it will literally change who you are by helping you focus on others instead of yourself.

You may wonder what's the harm in talking about yourself and feel like it's wrong to hide all the good things you do. You may even worry that if you don't draw attention to your own accomplishments, no one will ever take notice. That may be true because other people may be just as focused on all the good they are doing. This is your chance to turn the tide. When you focus on the good that someone else is doing, they will feel acknowledged and appreciated—and they may start noticing the good that you do. If they don't, that's fine. Being more humble will help you notice more of the great and wonderful things others are doing in the world.

FlipSide

List the good in others

Emotional

Social

Occupational

The Flip Side Challenge invites you to write down one good thing about someone who annoys you—each day for the next 30 days. Think of a person who does things that bother you or just doesn't do things like you would. Then find a time each day to write down the person's name and something good about that person. Consider focusing on the same person for the entire challenge—a potentially powerful exercise. If you find it daunting to come up with 30 good things about that one person, you can write about different people each day.

Your brain naturally categorizes information to make it easier to recall. Unfortunately, your brain does this with people too. When a person behaves in a certain way, we're quick to label that person. From that point on, we look at them through a particular lens—noticing actions that support the label and ignoring the good they do. The goal of this challenge is to help you stop looking through critical lenses at people and focus on the good things they do instead of the annoying things that bother you. Get ready for the world to look brighter and better!

Freshly**Squeezed**
Hug someone daily

Social

Physical

The Freshly Squeezed Challenge invites you to hug one person each day for the next 30 days. It doesn't matter if you hug the same person each day or 30 different people, just hug someone each day. Greet people with a hug. Give support with a hug. Congratulate with a hug. Thirty is quite a few, so don't pass up an opportunity. If it seems awkward, explain that you are doing a challenge and most people will be willing to help you out. (Note: Depending on your work environment and your position within your company, hugging may not be appropriate at work.)

Hugging can strengthen relationships and heal broken relationships through the bond it creates and the chemical changes that happen inside the body. When you hug someone, oxytocin—known as the bliss hormone—is released and helps us feel less stressed and happier. Even just knowing that someone wants to hug you can give you an emotional boost. Hugging can also help you and those that you've just hugged feel more comfortable around each other. Reach out and hug someone today and experience the difference it makes.

Give30

Give daily

Emotional

Social

The Give 30 Challenge invites you to give daily for the next 30 days. You can give a physical gift or the gift of service to others or to the earth. You can start each day with no particular plan, but if you take the time to plan ahead, your gifts will likely be more meaningful to you and to the recipient. Bring cookies to a neighbor, buy coffee for someone at work, pick up loose trash in your neighborhood, or plant a tree. Consider teaming up with a friend or family member (even a child) to do this challenge—and give daily together.

Giving helps us focus on others instead of ourselves, freeing our physical and emotional selves from self-servitude—the most unrelenting of all masters. The freedom you get from forgetting your own needs is exhilarating. If you feel like you're already a pretty giving person, challenge yourself to take it up a notch. Spend a little more time or money than you usually would. After all, it's only for 30 days—unless you get hooked and keep doing it for the rest of your life!

Good**Connection**

Talk with your partner daily

Emotional

Social

The Good Connection Challenge invites you to speak with your partner daily. There's no time requirement for how long you should talk, but hopefully it's more than a quick, "I love you"—although those are certainly wonderful words to say. The purpose of the daily check-in is to increase communication between the two of you—hopefully strengthening your relationship. You can share your day's activities, coordinate your weekend plans, talk about the future, or discuss concerns or current events. Talk in person, if you can, but if that's not possible, have your conversation over the phone. In a pinch, you can even text each other. Be sure to express your feelings for each other as well!

Life goes by fast and if you don't consciously take the time to talk with your partner, it won't happen. Maybe that's okay if it happens now and then, but over time if you don't communicate, you can drift apart. It's natural. What brought you together was spending time together, and if you stop spending time together what you had will disappear. Conversely, if you make the effort to be together, your relationship will flourish—making both of your lives more enjoyable. So make some time for your partner today!

Good**Intro**

Give 5 high-quality introductions

Social

The Good Intro Challenge invites you to give a good, thorough introduction for five people who you know. You can introduce anyone you know to someone else. If you introduce two people who you know to each other, you get to count both! When you introduce the person you know, share interesting facts—point out some of their strengths, and express appreciation for them. At first it may feel awkward to provide so much information about them, but after a few of these detailed introductions, it will become a nice experience for all involved. The extra time will be well worth it.

When you take the time to give a nice introduction, all parties benefit: the person being introduced is honored, the person receiving the introduction gains a good idea right away of who they are meeting, and the person doing the introduction receives the joy of giving. The more thoughtful the introduction is, the more everyone benefits. Just like everything else, practice makes perfect—you will become better at making introductions the more you do them. Start practicing today!

Gratitude Partner

Exchange gratitude notes

Emotional

Social

The Gratitude Partner Challenge invites you to have an exchange with your partner, sharing one reason you're grateful for each other, each day for the next 30 days. If you don't have a significant other, do this with a family member or a close friend. You can have this exchange in person or over the phone, but a written text or email can be more effective. Receiving a text or email can be the other's cue to respond with their message of gratitude—and at the end of the month all the reasons you're grateful for each other will be written down. You could even write little sticky notes for each other. Feel free to be creative!

It's natural to notice others' weaknesses—whether we verbalize them or keep them inside. With a little habit-building magic, you can switch gears and focus on the positive instead. As you zero in on what you're grateful for, life will become more pleasant and positive for you and everyone around you. Enriching your close relationships by expressing gratitude is vital because these close relationships can either be your biggest source of pain or your biggest source of joy. Choose joy by expressing your gratitude every day!

Hard**Question**

Ask thought-provoking questions

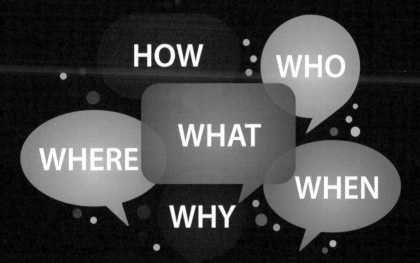

The Hard Question Challenge invites you to ask one person a day a thought-provoking question for the next 30 days. You can ask the same person all 30 questions or ask different people—both approaches have unique benefits. If you miss a day, you can ask two questions the next day. The intent of the thought-provoking question is to get the other person to think for a bit, then share their thoughts with you so you can grow your relationship. As they talk, be sure to *really* listen—allow them to complete their thoughts without interruption. Ask follow-up questions if it feels right or just thank them for sharing.

Relationships become stronger as we share our innermost thoughts, but we rarely share these deep thoughts because we don't want them to be judged or criticized. We need to feel safe with another person before we share what's deep inside. When you show someone that you're interested in and respect their opinion, you've created such an environment. It may take some effort on your part to think of good questions for each person, but it will be worth it. Think of all the interesting perspectives you will gain in the next 30 days!

Social

Occupational

BallotBox

Vote in an election

The Ballot Box Challenge invites you to vote in an election. This can be a local election or a general election. Prepare yourself beforehand by researching who is running for office and which measures and propositions will be on the ballot. If you aren't sure about who or which proposal is best, read about them online and talk to trusted friends and relatives to gain their perspectives. Vote for what coincides with your beliefs and hopes for your community and country. It's your right and your privilege as a citizen.

If you are not registered to vote, be sure to register before the deadline. You can opt to vote by absentee ballot if that works better for you. This will allow you to fill out the ballot at home or abroad and mail it in. If you don't meet the mail-in deadline for some reason, you can bring it to a voting booth on Election Day. It's essential that you follow the instructions for marking your ballot so your vote counts. One of the many freedoms we enjoy in our country is to participate in the election process—so get out and vote!

Little**Buddy**

Spend time with a child

Purpose

Emotional

Social

The Little Buddy Challenge invites you to spend time with a child. If you have children, use this challenge to spend some quality time with one of them. If you aren't a parent, ask if you can spend some time with a friend or family member's child. Plan something the child will enjoy—go somewhere fun, eat some yummy food together, or go on an outdoor adventure. Ask the child what they would like to do, as they may prefer something simple like reading, playing, or doing art.

The goal of this challenge is to change your adult perspective on life as you slow down (or speed up!) and see life as a child does. Often as adults we overcomplicate things. Hopefully, being around a child will help remind you to keep it simple and focus on the things in life that really matter. Our relationships are definitely at the top of that list. Keep this in mind as you build a relationship with this child—a relationship that may impact you both for the rest of your life!

May|

Ask how you can help

Emotional

Social

The May I Challenge invites you to ask one person each day for the next 30 days if you can help them. Think of the question as a conversation ender. When you're wrapping up a conversation, just ask, "Is there anything I can do to help you?" At first it may seem awkward, but eventually it will feel just fine and natural. Most people will say they are fine and don't need anything, but insist that you'd like to help them with whatever may come up. Once they understand that you are truly willing to help, they may reach out to you later on. If you miss asking someone one day, just ask two people the next day.

When you ask people if there is any way that you can help them, most people will be taken aback initially, but after they reflect on your request, they will appreciate your offer and respect you for it. Hopefully, it will help them realize that it's okay to ask for help. We have a desire deep within us to help other people. Most of us would do things for others that we wouldn't even do for ourselves. It's part of who we are as humans. As you act on this desire, you will become more in touch with your true self and more at peace with yourself and the world.

PenPal
Write 4 letters

Emotional

Social

The Pen Pal Challenge invites you to write and send four letters in the next 30 days via *regular mail*. Pick four people who you think would appreciate getting a real letter. It could be someone older who loves getting letters in the mail or someone who has never received a handwritten letter. Consider writing your letter on some fun stationary, using a colorful pen, or maybe even decorating the envelope. Writing your letter by hand is optimal, but if you must type it, be sure to add your signature at the end after you've printed it. (Email isn't allowed for this challenge.) You don't need to write a novel, but write enough that it is indeed a letter, not a note.

Writing letters is becoming a lost art form. These days there are people who have never written a letter to a friend or relative and many more who have never received one. The process of writing a letter will be beneficial to you. It will demand that you organize your thoughts and consider what you'll say more than you would in a conversation or text. This is a good thing because the recipients of your letters will probably read the letter more than once and may even choose to save it. Don't let this process intimidate you—just get out your pen and start writing. This challenge may leave a lasting impression on the people you write to and on you!

Family History
Record a relative's story

The Family History Challenge invites you to record part or all of a relative's life story. Think of a relative you admire and ask them if they'd be willing to let you record them telling stories from their life. Prepare a list of questions and set a time to talk in person or virtually. Plan how you're going to record the conversation—one of the simplest ways is with your smartphone. You could even video the interview if your relative is open to being filmed. To complete the challenge, all you need to do is conduct the interview and record the responses, but you could take it further by transcribing the conversation and maybe even asking the relative to edit the transcription.

Helping a family member record their life story not only benefits them, but also your entire family. You enjoy learning about their experiences and will gain an understanding about their background. It may even help you better understand why you are the way you are. There is nothing like a family bond—no matter what happens, you're still family. These strong connections help strengthen us throughout our lives and actually help form who we are—even in adoptive relationships. Schedule an interview today with one of your relatives and find out more about your history!

PositiveIntent

Give others the benefit of the doubt

Emotional

Social

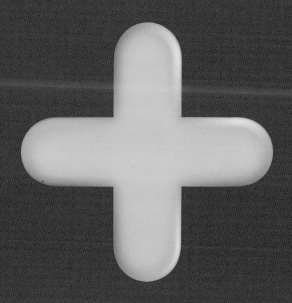

The Positive Intent Challenge invites you to write down one thing someone did that bothers you and a possible valid reason for why they did it—once a day for the next 30 days. If you can't think of anything from that particular day, you can use a situation from a previous day. Even if you don't feel bothered or upset, you can choose a situation where you viewed a person as being selfish or negative. Make sure you write it down as this will help you process your thoughts more thoroughly.

As we go through life we mess up occasionally, but we often believe we have a valid reason for doing what we did. When others mess up, however, they can seem rude, selfish, and even downright awful at times. Is this reality, or is it a picture we've created ourselves? Did that person really just cut you off on the freeway because he was impatient? Or was he rushing to get his daughter to the hospital? The goal of this challenge is to help you give others the benefit of the doubt. With a more positive perspective, you will feel happier inside, appreciate others more, and be more at peace with the world.

Paper**Less**

Avoid using paper

Social

Occupational

The Paper Less Challenge invites you to minimize the amount of paper you use for the next 30 days. These days, many paperless options exist. Instead of printing documents, read them on your computer. Take notes electronically. Keep your to-do list on your phone or computer. Use the revisions feature to give feedback on documents. Opt for electronic tickets when traveling. Choose to have receipts emailed to you at stores offering this option. Sign documents electronically. Use your creativity and figure out how you can avoid using paper.

We often use paper because that's simply what we've always done. You might think it's faster, easier, or more secure. You may also simply prefer a printed document. This challenge invites you to give the electronic alternative a try. Who knows? You may like it better! The electronic alternative often has several advantages to balance out any disadvantages. Signing documents electronically may save you time without having to use a scanner. Get out of your comfort zone and try something different—and save a few trees in the process!

RippleEffect

Send a positive text message

Emotional

Social

The Ripple Effect Challenge invites you to send one positive text message each day for the next 30 days. It doesn't matter who you send it to, just make sure the message you write is uplifting. If you miss a day, send two the next day. Tell someone how much you appreciate them, compliment them on something they've done, or wish them a wonderful day. If you can't think of 30 different people, you can send texts to the same person more than once. Imagine what the ripple effect of your 30 positive messages might be!

Writing something positive will help you feel more positive, knowing that it will brighten someone else's day and yours as well! Each person who reads the message you sent will feel more valued, more confident, and may start to send positive ripples out to others. Amazingly, when we send positive vibes out into the universe they tend to bounce back into our lives. As you send out positive energy in this challenge, pay attention to see if some of that positive energy comes back to you. Think what a wonderful influence you can have in others' lives as you broadcast positivity to those around you!

ServeNProtect

Thank 3 public servants

Emotional

Social

The Serve N Protect Challenge invites you to thank three public servants. All you have to do is find three different people who work in civil service and thank them for what they do. It could be a police officer, firefighter, city employee, teacher, bus driver, person in the military, or park ranger. If you don't normally encounter such individuals, you may need to plan a special outing— for example, you could bring cookies to the fire station. You could also simply walk into your child's school office and tell some of the staff how much you appreciate them. Although this may be out of your comfort zone, you will see how much joy a simple thank you can bring, and you will want to do this again and again.

Public servants generally get paid less than they would if they worked in the private sector. Most choose to do public service because they enjoy serving others and want to help their community in some way. These people deserve recognition and a special thank you for what they do each day. Take a few moments to make someone's day brighter by showing your appreciation. In the process, your eyes will be opened and your heart will be softened toward the many civil servants around you who serve you and your community.

Small**Favor**

Help 5 people for 5 minutes

Emotional

Social

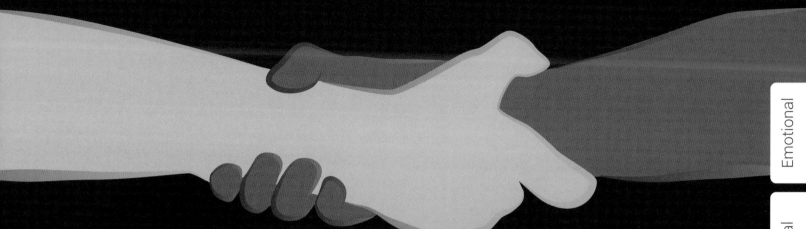

The Small Favor Challenge invites you to help five people for five minutes each in the next 30 days. The idea is to get in the practice of always looking for small and simple ways to help other people. We are all busy, but we can all find five minutes to help another person. Let someone go in front of you in line at the store or the post office, put in a good word for someone, review a co-worker's slide deck, make an introduction for a friend, help your child with homework, or load groceries into an elderly person's car. Your small favor may be just the boost another person needs.

For some, this challenge may be quite difficult because we tend to go through life focused only on ourselves. Even when we do help others, we tend to do it on our own terms, that is, when, where, how, and who we have decided to help. Instead, change your mindset to first look for what someone else needs. As you shift your focus from yourself to others, magical things happen. You will understand other people better, you will become happier, and life will become easier—paradoxical, but pretty remarkable. Do a few small favors and see how good you feel!

CHALLENGE
52

Skin**Deep**

Don't comment on appearance

Emotional

Social

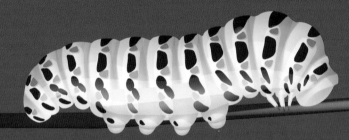

The Skin Deep Challenge invites you to *not* comment on anyone's appearance for 30 days. That's right, you can't tell anyone their hair looks nice, that you notice they've lost weight, or that you like their new shoes. On the surface, this challenge sounds wrong because we've been taught all our lives to compliment people. The goal here is to compliment someone on something that's *deeper* than how they look, like how thoughtful, generous, or smart they are. You could also comment on someone's punctuality, dedication, or reliability. If you slip up and comment on someone's appearance, add a deeper compliment to make up for it.

This simple challenge can be transformative. While it's natural to judge people on their outward appearance since it's the first thing we see, focusing on character attributes is far more complimentary. As you consciously refrain from commenting on anyone's appearance, you'll realize how deeply the pernicious habit of judging has embedded itself into your life. With this realization, you can look beyond appearance at what really matters about people. You may be surprised at how good this feels—like a giant burden has been lifted!

Take**One**

Use a single disposable

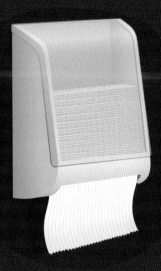

The Take One Challenge invites you to use a single disposable napkin when dining and a single paper towel when drying your hands in the washroom. If you end up needing more napkins when you eat, just take one at a time as you need them instead of a bunch at the beginning of the meal that you may never need. Using cloth napkins is better yet! Do the same when drying your hands. A single paper towel may be plenty to dry your hands, even if it becomes completely saturated in the process. Better yet, use an electric hand dryer whenever possible.

When dining out, it's easy to get into the habit of grabbing a big stack of napkins, just in case. The same is true when drying your hands—you may be taking more paper towels than you need. You can reduce a tremendous amount of waste if you only take what you absolutely need! Imagine the trees you will save and the landfills you will lighten over your lifetime, not to mention the fossil fuels used in the creation, delivery, and disposal process. Take *one* for the team!

Video**Call**

Have 5 video calls

Emotional

Social

The Video Call Challenge invites you to have five video calls in the next 30 days. You can use an app on your mobile phone or a meeting tool on your PC—most of these tools are free. This will most likely require some advanced planning on your part to make sure the other person is willing and able to participate. The calls can be remote meetings for work or leisure calls to your friends and family. There's no time limit for the calls.

If you've ever engaged in a video call, you know it's a much richer experience than a regular voice call. You can see what the other person is doing, where they are, and can enjoy each other's facial expressions. You're also more likely to give them your full attention, because the other person will know if you're multitasking. Although we often choose a regular voice call because it's easier or it's what we're used to doing, this challenge will get you to try video calls. Who knows? Maybe you'll like video calls and use them more often!

YayYou

Celebrate someone else

Emotional

Social

The Yay You Challenge invites you to identify someone who has had something good happen in their life and then choose a way to celebrate it with them. Do you know anyone who just got promoted, aced a test, was selected for a team, had a child graduate, moved into a new home, or had a new baby? All of these things are cause for celebration! Think of how you might celebrate that person—go out for lunch, give them a card, organize a party, bake a cake, give them a gift, or anything else that sounds fun.

This challenge is a great way to get yourself thinking about others and celebrating them instead of thinking mainly about yourself. Focusing on others instead of yourself, your troubles, and your worries is a healthy practice to get into. When you're noticing another person's success, be careful that you don't compare yourself with them! Another person's achievement doesn't take away from anything you do. Besides, it's not about you—the more you come to understand this, the happier you will be in life. Who will you celebrate?

You're**Right**

Do not counter others' ideas

Emotional

Social

Occupational

The You're Right Challenge invites you to simply accept others' ideas instead of countering them for the next 30 days. Pointing out holes in other people's thoughts is impolite and is a huge cultural epidemic. One person says, "It's so nice out today," and the person with them says, "I think it's too humid." Watch for this pattern and you'll see it happen all the time. Your goal here is to stop the cycle and just take in what other people say. If you don't agree, say nothing. If you do, nod your head or tell them you agree. This may be more challenging than you think and it will help you in ways you can't imagine!

It seems harmless to refute others' ideas—you probably feel like you're just having a healthy exchange of thoughts or even doing them a favor by pointing something out, but they're not looking for correction or a critique. They're looking to be heard. Why don't we just listen? Hear what they are saying, ponder why they might be saying it, and ask questions to gain further understanding. With habits like this, you'll become the person everyone wants to be around because they feel so good when they talk with you!

Zip|t

Don't interrupt others

The Zip It Challenge invites you to *not* interrupt others for 30 days. All you have to do is not say anything while others are talking. It sounds easy, but for some people it can be incredibly hard. When someone else talks, you'll need to wait until they've finished their thought, then you can say what you'd like. If you're like most people, this will be a difficult challenge and you will slip up and interrupt at times. As long as you are trying, you can count your efforts as good for the day.

When we listen to others speak, we often spend our time thinking about what we're going to say next. When something comes to mind, we can't wait to say it and often cut off others to do it. Ideally, instead of thinking about what we are going to say next, we should be focusing our full attention on what the person is saying. Questions will naturally come to mind as you seek to understand what the other person is saying. Instead of just blurting out what you feel you need to say, hold your tongue until they are finished speaking. Your conversations will reach new depths, you'll learn more, and your discussions will become more satisfying. Everyone will want to spend time talking with you!

Bad**Fat**

Avoid hydrogenated fats

Nutrition Facts		
Serving Size **50g**		
Amount per serving		
Calories 235	Calories from fat 12	
		% Daily Value
Total fat 2g		4%
Saturated fat 2g		4%
Trans Fat 0g		
Cholesterol 0mg		0%
Sodium 0mg		0%
Total Carbohydrate 19g		3%
Dietary Fiber 2g		6%
Sugars 17g		
Protein 29g		
Vitamin C 35%	**Vitamin A** 20%	
Calcium 5%	**Zinc** 5%	

Physical

The Bad Fat Challenge invites you to not eat any hydrogenated fat for 30 days. If you prepare your own food, you pretty much just need to avoid using shortening or margarine. Read the labels on your packaged foods, watching out for trans fats, partially hydrogenated fat, shortening, and hydrogenated oils. When you eat out, avoid fried foods and baked goods. Even if a label claims "No Trans Fat," be sure to check it carefully as fully hydrogenated fat contains no trans fats, but is still not good for your health.

Hydrogenated fat is made by a chemical process that forces hydrogen atoms into an inexpensive oil to make it solid at room temperature. This gives the oil greater stability for frying and is preferable in baking. However, oils that come from nature (olive, avocado, sunflower, and real butter, to name a few) that have not been hydrogenated are healthier choices. The goal of this challenge is to increase your awareness of hydrogenated fats and to learn to choose foods that contain healthy fats instead.

Bedtime**Story**

Read before going to bed

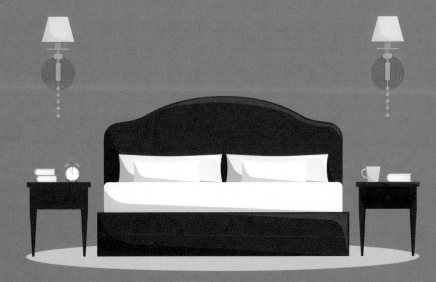

The Bedtime Story Challenge invites you to read before going to bed for 30 days. After your normal bedtime routine, relax somewhere comfy and read for a while. You can read whatever you like, but since it's the end of the day, you may want to choose something that helps you unwind. A real book is ideal, but if you'd rather use an electronic reader, be sure to use the nighttime color filter so the light doesn't stimulate your brain and make it more difficult for you to sleep. When you feel drowsy or have grown tired of reading, head off to bed. Continue this practice for a month and see what it does for you.

There is a reason that parents read bedtime stories to their children at night. It calms them down and helps them go to sleep. The same is true for adults—reading can calm the mind and prepare the body for a soothing, restful slumber. Who doesn't need a good night's sleep? Reading is also great for your brain. Decoding and processing the information is literally exercise for your brain. In addition to being educational, reading can also be entertaining and fun. Use this challenge as a chance to catch up on any books you've been wanting to read. You'll get the bonus of sleeping better and becoming smarter at the same time!

Physical

Occupational

CHALLENGE
60

Big**Stink**

Eat cruciferous vegetables

Physical

The Big Stink Challenge invites you to eat one cruciferous vegetable a day for the next 30 days. Some common cruciferous vegetables are: cauliflower, cabbage, kale, bok choy, broccoli, Brussels sprouts, and turnips. Prepare them ahead of time to have handy for snacks by washing and slicing, roasting, or putting together in a salad. If you don't love raw veggies, try dipping them in some hummus or Greek yogurt. Shred some cabbage in advance (or buy it pre-shredded), so you can make a quick salad by adding a little dressing. Look for kale salads in many restaurants. If you are a fan of fresh sauerkraut or kimchee, you could get an added nutritional boost of natural probiotics!

Cruciferous vegetables are chock full of health benefits! They are high in vitamin C and soluble fiber, contain multiple nutrients and phytochemicals, and have been shown to prevent certain types of cancer. (If you are taking any prescription medications, consult your physician before doing this challenge since cruciferous vegetables may reduce the effectiveness of certain drugs.) You might not continue eating cruciferous vegetables every day after this challenge, but hopefully you will learn new ways to enjoy them more often since they are so good for you!

Can**Caffeine**

No caffeine from a can

Physical

The Can Caffeine Challenge invites you to not drink any canned or bottled beverages that contain caffeine for 30 days. Caffeinated sodas contain between 30 mg and 55 mg of caffeine in a standard 12-ounce can. Energy drinks and energy shots contain anywhere from 75 mg to more than 400 mg of caffeine. Caffeine has been shown to improve mental alertness and cognitive performance, and an intake of 400 mg or less per day is currently considered safe, but too much caffeine may not be good for your body. In particular, it may mask your body's need for appropriate rest, lead to withdrawal headaches, and exacerbate anxiety and insomnia.

You need to be able to recognize your body's signals so you can know how to care for it. If caffeine has been your go-to energizer, try out some new ways to improve your mental alertness. Exercise in the morning, take a catnap, drink more water, eat healthier foods, take a walk during your break, do some yoga, take a digital detox, or go to bed earlier. It may not be easy at first, but after a few days your body will be more in tune with its needs and you will feel better. Kick the can and tune into how your body really feels!

FreshAir

Walk outside 20 minutes a day

Physical

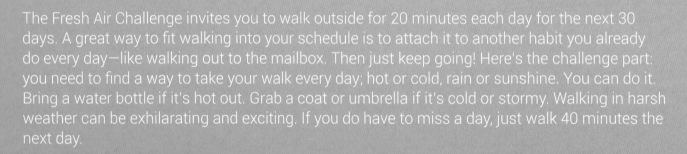

The Fresh Air Challenge invites you to walk outside for 20 minutes each day for the next 30 days. A great way to fit walking into your schedule is to attach it to another habit you already do every day—like walking out to the mailbox. Then just keep going! Here's the challenge part: you need to find a way to take your walk every day; hot or cold, rain or sunshine. You can do it. Bring a water bottle if it's hot out. Grab a coat or umbrella if it's cold or stormy. Walking in harsh weather can be exhilarating and exciting. If you do have to miss a day, just walk 40 minutes the next day.

We all know that walking is good for us, but we often forget about the tremendous health benefits of spending time outdoors. Being out in nature can help you relax and clear your mind. You can get valuable vitamin D if it's sunny and be invigorated by inclement weather. Your natural surroundings can both stimulate and calm your body and mind. Doing this challenge during a month when the weather is typically good will certainly have its benefits, but if you're up for a greater challenge then choose a month that is typically hot, cold, snowy, or rainy. These are the times that a walk outside could invigorate you the most. Take a walk!

Fruit30

Eat 30 different fruits

The Fruit 30 Challenge invites you to try 30 different fruits over the next 30 days. The first dozen or so will be easy to find, then it may become a challenge to figure out what other fruits to eat. Wander the produce section of your grocery store to look for more varieties of fruits. Check out a health food store or ethnic grocery store for even more options. You might find other varieties of a familiar fruit at a farmer's market. Watch what other people choose and ask them questions. The great thing about fruit is that it often requires little preparation and is naturally sweet. You may even find a new favorite fruit to add to your diet!

Fruits are high in vitamins and minerals. They have sugar, but it's a naturally occurring sugar and it usually comes with fiber and valuable nutrients. Unless you have diabetes or another health concern, you will be able to enjoy the sweetness of any fruit with no worry or guilt. Eating a wide variety of fruits will provide more health benefits (clearer skin, better digestion, more energy, disease prevention). Plus, you'll get to enjoy a multitude of flavors. To ensure variety, try to eat fruit from all the colors of the rainbow. Expand your horizons by eating 30 different fruits and watch for all the benefits to your health!

Physical

GoNuts

Eat 20 servings of nuts

Physical

The Go Nuts Challenge invites you to eat 20 servings of nuts over the next 30 days. All nuts have similar calorie content, so feel free to begin by just eating your favorite kinds. If you prefer peanut butter to eating peanuts, find one without added sugar or hydrogenated oils. The trick with nuts is to not eat too many since they're high in calories. One serving is about ¼ cup of nuts or two tablespoons of nut butter and contains about 200 calories. Nuts are a great snack to keep in your bag to help tide you over to your next meal, as the fiber, fat, and protein all help you feel full despite eating small quantities.

Nuts are a great source of antioxidants, protein, fiber, vitamins, and minerals. Nuts are also high in healthy monounsaturated and polyunsaturated fats (including omega-3 fatty acids, which are particularly high in walnuts). These are the kinds of fat that help lower LDL or "bad" cholesterol levels, reducing the risk of heart disease and inflammation. Diets rich in nuts have also been associated with a lower risk of cancer. However, be wary of nuts with too much salt. Try unsalted nuts and even raw nuts (nuts that haven't been roasted). You'll discover variances in flavor and may find a new favorite. Grab a handful and go nuts!

Hands Free

No mobile phone while driving

The Hands Free Challenge invites you to not touch your phone while you are driving—not for a phone call, not for texting, not for music, not for directions, not for anything! You can only touch your phone when your car is fully stopped and in Park. Try putting your phone away in your bag or in the glove compartment. Turn off the audio notifications so you're not tempted to check it. If you can't wait until you arrive at your destination, pull over and check it while you're safely stopped.

For most drivers, this will be a hard habit to break, since we're constantly using our phones. In most places, using a mobile phone while driving is against the law since a large percentage of car accidents today are caused by people who are distracted by their phone. Still, we can't seem to stop. We have a fear of missing out, we need to know everything instantly, and we're always seeking entertainment. No one believes how truly dangerous it is, but a few seconds of distraction could cause a deadly crash. This challenge is more than a healthy habit, it's a matter of life or death.

Physical

Heads Up
No smartphone while walking

The Heads Up Challenge invites you to *not* use your smartphone while walking, and, yes, this includes talking on your phone too. It seems harmless to use your smartphone while walking, but it's actually more dangerous than you think. Companies that have implemented a "hands-free" walking policy have seen a dramatic decrease in accidents. Think about it—not looking where you are going or noticing what's going on around you is a bad idea. Talking on your phone while walking may seem safe because you can see where you're going, but it's a big distraction and has resulted in many injuries and even deaths.

Walking can be a wonderful way to enjoy nature, relax your mind, and greet others—but not if you're using your smartphone. Walking can be healing for the soul if you are present and soak in your surroundings—taking in the sounds, sights, smells, and temperature—instead of counting "likes". Let go of your usual concerns, plans, and worries and just enjoy the experience of walking, allowing it to be meditative and relaxing. If you'd like to get your heart rate up, quicken your pace a bit. Walking is one of the simple pleasures of life—enjoy it!

HungryJack

Track your hunger

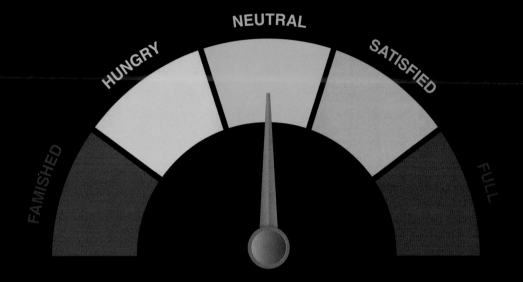

The Hungry Jack Challenge invites you to track your hunger level before and after you eat. You can eat whatever you'd like and whenever you want; you just need to note your hunger level before you eat and again afterward. Identify if you are: (1) *famished* (you would eat anything in sight), (2) *hungry* (you could eat a full meal), (3) *neutral* (not hungry but you'd be tempted by the right snack), (4) *satisfied* (comfortable and content), or (5) *full* (uncomfortably full). Record your hunger levels in a notebook or on your phone, whatever is most convenient for you.

Tracking your hunger is an awareness exercise. Many of us routinely eat when we're *not hungry*. Ideally, we should wait until we *are* hungry (but before we become famished) to eat. To avoid overeating, we should eat slowly and pay attention to when we no longer feel hungry. It generally takes around 20 minutes for your hunger cues to subside after eating. Physically pushing your plate away from you and saying out loud, "That's plenty for me; I've eaten enough" will help you reinforce the idea that your meal is complete and can help you avoid eating until you are stuffed. Tuning into your hunger signals can eliminate the need to diet for the rest of your life!

Physical

Lead Foot

Obey the speed limit

SPEED LIMIT 35

Emotional

Social

Physical

The Lead Foot Challenge invites you to not exceed the speed limit when driving for 30 days. If you're not perfect, that's fine—just keep trying. The idea is to become more conscious of abiding by the speed limit wherever you go. A simple way to remember is to post a reminder note by your speedometer. If you're used to driving fast, plan extra time for trips so you don't feel rushed. Let others know what you're up to so they can support you (or even join you!). This may be quite a challenge and the first time you've attempted something like this, but you can do it!

Imagine not having to keep an eye on a navigation app while you drive or keep a look out for a police car. Even if you did see a police car, you could relax knowing that you are driving at or even below the speed limit—wouldn't that be nice? Do you really need the extra few minutes or seconds you gain by speeding? Notice the people who speed past you. Often you end up at the same stoplight later on, waiting together. Also, consider that if you're in an accident, you could be at fault if you were speeding. Is the gain worth your safety and integrity? Straighten up, be true to yourself, and don't exceed the speed limit. Life's too short to speed!

No**Sweat**

Exercise 600 minutes without sweating

Physical

The No Sweat Challenge invites you to exercise 20 minutes a day for the next 30 days—without ever breaking a sweat. If you've been too busy to fit a regular workout into your daily routine, this is the challenge for you. You can add low-impact, low-intensity exercises into your normal day without going to a gym. You can attach this activity to something you already do regularly and create a new daily habit that's easy to keep up. If you don't get in the full 20 minutes one day, just add it to the next day.

Here are some ideas: Before getting a drink of water or when you are on a conference call, do a few push-ups, squats, wall sits, or planks; take the stairs instead of the elevator; park at the back of the parking lot or walk around the block before going into work; take a five-minute walk when you are low on energy; or hold a walking meeting. Get creative! There are a multitude of options and they will add up. Pretty soon, getting a workout in will seem like no sweat at all.

Periodic**Fast**

Take a break from food

The Periodic Fast Challenge invites you to try periodic fasting five times over the next 30 days. You can choose whatever method of intermittent fasting you like, but two popular formats are to: (1) fast for 16 hours (skip breakfast or dinner); or (2) fast for 24 hours (skip breakfast and lunch). Be sure to stay hydrated by drinking lots of plain water throughout the day. If you have a health condition like diabetes or you are pregnant, it may not be wise for you to fast, so be sure to check with your doctor as this may not be the challenge for you. For most healthy people, though, brief fasts are fine and can be good for your health.

Some diets prescribe several small meals throughout the day. Periodic fasting is just the opposite. Both approaches can work as long as you limit your total caloric intake. Which method you use depends on what best fits your lifestyle. Fasting on occasion makes it easier for some to be in tune with and to regulate how much they eat. Also, some say that the body needs about 12 hours of not eating in order to deplete its short-term energy stores so it can burn fat. Others say that it's beneficial to give our digestive systems a break even if we're not trying to lose weight. Give fasting a try and see if it works for you!

PhotoFinish

Photograph everything you eat

The Photo Finish Challenge invites you to take a picture of everything you eat for 30 days. You can eat whatever you like, whenever you like, just take a picture of it first. If you have seconds, take a picture. If you want a snack, take a picture. If you forget, write down what you ate and take a picture of what you wrote. This challenge is a simpler version of calorie counting. Granted, you won't know your caloric intake, but that's okay. You'll be aware of what you eat, how often you eat, and how much you eat. This new awareness will hopefully help you be more mindful each time you decide to eat something.

Eating can be habitual. You see donuts on the counter and you eat one. There's food still on the table, so you take seconds. You're watching television, so you grab something to snack on. At the movie theater you eat popcorn and candy. This challenge will help you be more mindful of all of these patterns—the when, what, and how much you eat. After all, awareness is the first step to making a change. If you want to get more insight and support, show your pictures to a coach or friend who has some expertise with nutrition. They'll help you find ways to improve your diet and may even help you stay accountable.

Physical

PlantFood

Eat vegan for one day

The Plant Food Challenge invites you to try a vegan diet for one day. A vegan diet is stricter than being a vegetarian. In addition to not eating any meat, a vegan diet also excludes any other animal products like eggs, dairy, and even honey. It will be eye-opening as you check labels and ask questions at restaurants to understand the ingredients that are in your food. To fully understand what it's like to be a vegan, make sure to include legumes (beans) on the day you try. Legumes are a good source of protein that most vegans include in their diet.

Don't worry. A vegan diet for a short time won't impact your health. Millions of people live their entire lives on a vegan diet. By the same token, don't worry that a diet including animal products is unhealthy either. Limited amounts of dairy, eggs, and meat are not detrimental to your health. So what's the point of this exercise? In general, most people eat more animal products than they need. Not only will this exercise make you more understanding of your vegan friends, it will also hopefully help you increase the amount of plant-based food you eat.

Plate|t

Present your food like a chef

The Plate It Challenge invites you to plate your food like a chef before bringing it to the table for the next 30 days. Plating is the practice of arranging food on your plate in a way that looks beautiful and delicious, like it would be presented to you in a restaurant. Consider pre-slicing your meat, sprinkling chopped parsley around the edge of the plate, making a design with the sauce, or forming your rice or potatoes into an interesting shape. Have some fun and arrange your food into a giant heart or smiley face on your plate. Imagine the family memories you will create! Consider building on this refined presentation by using cloth napkins and putting a wedge of lemon on your water.

The idea of cleverly presenting food on your plate goes beyond developing your creativity or being more formal. It indirectly eliminates seconds (and thirds!), like if you were at a restaurant. You and your family will have a lovely meal and learn portion control at the same time. Hopefully, the beautiful presentation (and knowing that there will be no seconds) will help your family slow down and savor their food. It will also be nice not to have to pass serving dishes around. Get ready to have some fun, be creative, and enjoy not feeling so stuffed after your meal!

SmileUps

Do smile exercises

Social

Physical

The Smile-Ups Challenge invites you to do 10 Smile-Ups every day for the next 30 days. If you're like most people, you're probably wondering what a Smile-Up is. To do a Smile-Up, smile big and wide, hold it for a count of three, and then relax your face muscles for three counts. Repeat 10 times for this challenge. If you forget one day, do two sets the following day to make it up. You may feel fatigued in your cheeks and mouth like you just blew up a bunch of balloons. That's great! It means you're working those facial muscles and are making progress. For even more fun, find a Smile-Ups buddy and look each other in the eyes while you do your Smile-Ups.

At first, Smile-Ups may sound silly, but they actually benefit your body. Smiling exercises can increase the blood flow to your face and give you a healthy glow. They can also improve your smile, lessen the lines in your face as you age, and strengthen the muscles in your face. Smiling also makes you feel happier—whether your smile is forced or not—by releasing endorphins into your body, chemicals that make us feel happy and lower stress levels. Hopefully doing Smile-Ups from time to time will encourage you to share big smiles more often!

*Smile-Ups[SM] is a registered service mark of Sarah Routman of Laugh Healthy.

Topsy Turvy

Get inverted

The Topsy Turvy Challenge invites you to do an inversion pose for a few minutes a day for 30 days. You can do a traditional yoga inversion pose or any variation that turns your body upside down in some way. Standing on both feet and folding forward from the hips is an inversion. Lying on the floor with your legs up against the wall or your feet on a chair or couch is a nice, relaxing inversion. Check the Internet for other inversion poses that may work for you.

Inversions are positions of the body where the heart is higher than the head or, if you're lying flat, the feet are higher than the heart. Inversions allow the blood to flow in a different way—helping deoxygenated blood from the lower body to passively flow back to the heart more efficiently. Some risks are associated with inversions for pregnant women or individuals with head or neck injuries, so either discuss this challenge with your physician for safety or hold off on this challenge. For the rest of us, though, inversions can be fun to try. See if inversions work for you!

Veg 30

Eat 30 different vegetables

Physical

The Veg 30 Challenge invites you to eat 30 different vegetables over the next 30 days. The first 10–15 will be easy and then this will start to become a real challenge. Peruse the produce section of your grocery store for ideas. You might consider a specialty or ethnic grocery store to find more options. Go to the Farmer's Market if it's the right time of year. When someone takes a vegetable you're not familiar with, ask them how they prepare it. Search the Internet to find out how to prepare vegetables that are new to you. Start early in the month as the last 10 vegetables may take longer to find and prepare.

Vegetables have the highest amount of vitamins, minerals, and micronutrients per calorie of all the food groups. Each vegetable has its own unique set of health benefits—not to mention its own distinctive flavor. Expanding your vegetable repertoire will give you a healthier body and will add variety to your meals. One way to make sure you're getting vegetables with various health properties is to eat vegetables that are all different colors. No matter which vegetables you choose, it will likely be a great boost to your health!

WaterFirst

Drink water before eating

The Water First Challenge invites you to drink a glass of water before eating anything, including snacks and meals. This practice can help you eat less. If you're prone to snacking, you may find you're not hungry after all when you've had some water first. The goal of this challenge is to build up the habit of drinking water before eating. If you keep forgetting, fill up a water bottle early in the day and leave it somewhere within plain sight, like on your desk or kitchen counter. Perhaps post a reminder note where you keep your snacks or on the table where you eat your meals.

Drinking water before a meal can help you feel more full and satisfied, reducing the amount of food you eat. This can help you eliminate unnecessary calories from your diet and may lead to weight loss. Also, we often think we're hungry when we may actually be dehydrated. Drinking a glass of water can help you feel satisfied, so you don't reach for snacks that you don't really need. Dehydration can also cause fatigue, so developing a habit of drinking more water can give you energy throughout the day. Grab a glass of water and say "Cheers!"

Physical

AccountabilityCoach

Report your progress

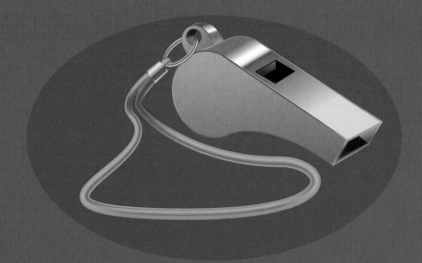

Emotional

Occupational

The Accountability Coach Challenge invites you to meet with a person of your choosing once a week for the next 30 days. Choose a family member, a friend, or even your boss. At your first meeting, commit to a list of things you would like to accomplish over the next week. Make sure to write the list down. Then go forward and work on your goals! In the subsequent meetings, review how well you did and commit to completing a new list of things to do the following week. Don't overcommit. Focus only on what you can do and then do it!

You'll be surprised at what you can accomplish. Making a commitment with another person to keep a goal, then returning to report your success creates accountability—and accountability helps us be successful. Believe it or not, many people in your life would be happy to help you be accountable. Likewise, you can help others with their goals by asking if they'd like an accountability coach. See how satisfying it can be for you and your helper!

Contact Us

Submit 3 ideas

CONTACT US

Social

Occupational

The Contact Us Challenge invites you to submit three ideas for improvement to one or more organizations you care about. First, choose an organization, then brainstorm some ideas that would help better that organization. Submit those ideas through their website or another means. Your perspective may be unique or something they've already considered. Either way it will be helpful to the organization to have your input. Use a positive tone with the ideas you offer so they sound like suggestions, not complaints. You can either submit three ideas to one organization or submit a single idea to three different organizations.

This challenge will stimulate your brain in several dimensions. First, it will require you to carefully consider the organizations that you would like to help, a means to learn facts about the institution that you may not have known before. Next, the creative part of your brain—a part that may be underused—will be activated as you come up with ideas. Finally, sharing the idea will move your brain into a benevolent mode—which can have a far-reaching impact for good. Put on your thinking cap and figure out who you'd like to help. Who knows? Maybe they'll actually implement your idea!

Early**Start**

Get to work 15 minutes early

The Early Start Challenge invites you to arrive at work 15 minutes early every day for the next 30 days. If you miss a day, get there 30 minutes early the next day to make up for it. When you arrive early, use the extra time to organize yourself for the day. Create a to-do list. Get caught up on any items you've been putting off. Organize your desk. Clear your inbox. Prepare for a meeting. You can even spend the time just pondering the day ahead of you or your life in general. Whatever you do with that time will give you an edge on the day.

When you start your day feeling prepared and organized, it's amazing how effective you can be throughout the day—and how much better you feel! This habit can help propel you in your career, as well. You'll get more done, advance more quickly, and be happier when you go home at the end of the day. Maybe this isn't something you'll continue to do for the rest of your career, but it can't hurt to give it a try for 30 days and watch what unfolds as a result.

Ernest**Hemingway**

Write a 5,000-word novel

The Ernest Hemingway Challenge invites you to write your own 5,000-word novel in the next 30 days. You're probably thinking there is no way you could write a novel—but you can! If you write one-third of a single-spaced page each day (167 words), you will reach your goal. You'll likely be more successful if you set a specific time each day to write. It will also be helpful to map out the storyline of your novel before you begin. Commit to writing for a certain amount of time (e.g., 15 minutes), whether you feel like doing it or not. If the juices are flowing when you hit your time limit, continue writing. If you've got writer's block, take a break and try again the next day.

Writing has so many benefits—it can make you happier, strengthen your brain, and reduce stress. A big benefit for this writing challenge will be a great sense of accomplishment! You will prove to yourself that you can do something that you never thought you could. That's empowering. It will put you in a "What next?" mindset, ready to tackle other endeavors that sound monumental. Ernest Hemingway said, "My aim is to put down on paper what I see and what I feel in the best and simplest way." So, what are you waiting for? Take this challenge, write a novel, and become a stronger, better you!

GenerationGap

Seek advice from other generations

Emotional

Social

Occupational

The Generation Gap Challenge invites you to ask for advice from two people, one from a younger generation and one from an older generation. For this challenge, we'll define a generation as 20 or more years. If you're too young to ask someone from a younger generation, then ask someone two generations (40 years) older than you in addition to someone 20 years older. Think of an issue that you've been concerned about lately—something meaningful to you. Then ask each one of your trusted advisors for their insight. Sincerely listen to their responses— you're likely to hear a perspective much different than your own.

It's natural for people to associate mainly with others their own age because we tend to have more in common with them. Even so, we're missing out by not interacting with people who have had a vastly different life experience. We don't know what it was like to live in the decades before we were born, nor do we truly know what it's like growing up in today's world. These varied life experiences can bring interesting insight and perspective to issues we're facing. Whether or not you actually take the advice is up to you—but you will definitely see things through new eyes. What wisdom will you find as you cross the generational boundary?

Good**Advice**

Seek insight from 5 people

The Good Advice Challenge invites you to seek insight from five people. First, you need to think of something that has been troubling you or a decision you can't seem to make. Next, think of five people you trust who have unique insight or knowledge that could be helpful to you. Meet with each person individually (a phone call is fine, too) or convene a single meeting with all five people at the same time.

You don't have to take the advice you get, yet receiving guidance can help you weigh things out in your mind to find the best solution. Sharing something you're struggling with can help build bonds with the people you reach out to. Collaboration will also strengthen your resolve to act and give you confidence about the decisions you make. Your insight is unique. Likewise, each person you ask for advice has a distinct perspective that may help you come up with a solution you may never have identified on your own.

CHALLENGE
84

Good Job

List what you like about your job

Pros

Emotional

Occupational

The Good Job Challenge invites you to write down one thing a day that you like about your job for the next 30 days—yes, even on the weekends! This is similar to keeping a gratitude journal, but focuses solely on your job. After a week or two of writing down the easy things that come to mind, it will get more difficult. This may encourage you to get in the habit of searching for things you like about your job on a daily basis. What if there are things you don't like about your job? They'll start to diminish as you focus on the positive.

Since our jobs are associated with *work*, we may think that, by definition, work is not or cannot be enjoyable. While at work we often think about other things we'd rather be doing, but work can be enjoyable! Shouldn't it be if we spend the majority of our waking hours there? You don't have to be all smiles all day at work, but you can learn to enjoy what you do. After all, happiness is a state of mind. If you find that your job really is that bad, consider looking for another position that you will enjoy more. Write down what you like about your job and see where it takes you.

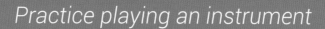

In Tune

Practice playing an instrument

The In Tune Challenge invites you to practice playing an instrument every day for the next 30 days. Set a minimum amount of time you will spend practicing, say five minutes. Even on days when you're not in the mood, practice at least five minutes, but if you are really into it continue longer. The goal is to have this become part of your daily routine so you'll be more likely to continue expanding your musical talents after the challenge. You can practice an instrument you already know how to play or learn to play a new one. If you need some help, sign up for a class or use online videos. If you don't have an instrument and are not sure if you want to buy one, consider renting one or borrowing one from a friend.

Playing an instrument has a multitude of benefits. It's like a workout for your brain; making you smarter, increasing your memory, and making you more creative. Playing music can reduce stress, alleviate depression, and soothe your soul. Music also gives you opportunities to interact socially if you decide to jam with others or just share. There's sheer grit involved in learning to practice an instrument, which increases your confidence, discipline, and time management skills. Playing an instrument is also fun! What instrument do you wish you could play?

CHALLENGE
86

Knowledge**Share**

Report what you learned

Emotional

Social

Occupational

The Knowledge Share Challenge invites you to learn something new and then present what you learned to a group. You can attend a conference, take a class, read a book, watch a webinar, or use any method of gaining knowledge. Then take the time to summarize what you learned—perhaps creating a slide deck or even just by jotting down some notes. Determine how much time you need for your presentation and invite a group of people to join you at work or within another organization. If you're excited to share your newfound knowledge, others will be excited to attend. Deliver your presentation and consider taking questions at the end to spark more learning.

Teaching others is a very powerful way to reinforce your learning. The process of organizing what you've learned into your own words will help you internalize and remember the concepts. Sharing your knowledge also gives you a chance to practice presenting, something most of us could benefit from. You'll be doing your peers a favor by summarizing mounds of information into concise gems that they can use in their lives. You may also develop new bonds with them as you share this experience. What knowledge will you share with your peers?

Lesson**Learned**

Take a class

The Lesson Learned Challenge invites you to take a class. It can be a training class for work or a leisure class that sounds interesting. If it's work related and the company you work for has a tight budget, propose taking an online class or a class taught locally to save on travel costs—and hopefully you'll get your manager's approval to pay for the course! If you'd rather take a leisure class just for fun, check your local library, city recreation center, or community college. Just don't choose a fitness class. (You can save that for a fitness challenge!)

Sometimes we're so busy with life and work that we forget about advancing our careers or continuing to grow through education. Pretty soon, years have passed and you notice that you haven't taken any time to better yourself. It's important to continue learning because it will help you avoid stagnation, do more in life, and reach towards your full potential. Learn something new by simply taking a class and see where it takes you!

Purpose

Emotional

Occupational

CHALLENGE
88

Life**Saver**

Take a CPR course

Social

Occupational

The Life Saver Challenge invites you to take a CPR (cardiopulmonary resuscitation) course. Look for a CPR course in your community—many fire departments teach CPR for free, but only a few times a year. You can also check with your local hospital, community college, or do an online search to see what's available in your area. Some employers sponsor a class at the workplace or even reimburse for off-site training. Search for a class with hands-on (versus video) learning so you'll get a chance to perform CPR and understand it much better. Most courses will include AED (automated external defibrillator) training as well.

CPR is a method of helping people who do not have a pulse and/or have stopped breathing; maybe from choking, drowning, or a heart attack. It is critical to start CPR as soon as possible after the heart stops beating to prevent brain damage. Without immediate CPR, the chance of someone without a heartbeat making it to the hospital alive is very low, so it is crucial to have someone nearby who can properly perform CPR. That person could be you! How amazing would it be if you were able to save another person's life?

PodCast

Listen to 10 podcasts

The Pod Cast Challenge invites you to listen to 10 podcasts in the next 30 days. Simply put, podcasts are spoken, audio episodes that often focus on a particular topic or theme. For this challenge, download a podcast app, browse for topics you might be interested in, and listen to 10 podcasts. It's that easy! Podcasts are simple to work into your day because you can listen to them while you're driving, walking, commuting, exercising, or doing household chores. In fact, doing other things while listening helps some people to better focus on the podcast!

Podcasts tend to be educational or informative in nature, which is great because people naturally love to learn. Learning is food for our souls, making us stronger inside and more resilient. As learning is most effective when we take small doses over time—listening to podcasts is a great way to fulfill this need. Ask around for others' favorite podcasts if you're not sure where to get started. There's a wealth of information out there. What will you learn about next?

Emotional

Occupational

Public**Speaker**

Give a speech

Emotional

Social

Occupational

The Public Speaker Challenge invites you to give a speech or presentation. Work with your boss to figure out something you can present internally or at a conference. You could also speak at a non-work organization of your choice. Your speech doesn't have to be long, but it should be at least five minutes so it has some depth. You can use notes, accompanying slides, or just deliver it from memory. Practice your speech in front of friends or family to make the actual presentation less stressful. You could even join Toastmasters!

Most people fear public speaking to one degree or another, but find it to be a rewarding experience. The benefits start long before you take the podium. Researching your topic and organizing your thoughts is a great mental exercise. It gives you a passion for learning about the topic that you might not have otherwise. You can also engage your creativity when you add visuals, music, or even storytelling techniques. Presenting in an engaging way to an audience is different than normal communication. It requires forethought and practice to do well. Become the master of your fear and go give a speech!

Single**Focus**

Give your full attention

The Single Focus Challenge invites you to make a special effort to focus when you are talking with someone for the next 30 days. Look in the person's eyes during the conversation, even if they aren't doing the same. When they are speaking, try to only listen to what they are saying rather than plan your response. Keep your focus on what they are saying, try to speak less, and ask more questions so you can learn more about the other person. Resist the temptation to find fault with or counter their points, just listen and observe. You won't do this perfectly in every conversation, but hopefully this challenge will help you move in the right direction.

In today's fast-paced, high-tech world, our attention spans are becoming shorter and shorter. We can hardly go a few minutes without getting a *hit* from our phones. We are easily distracted and often unable to do anything that requires extended focus. This challenge can help counteract this as you practice focusing your attention. Be patient with yourself. It's not easy, and it will take some effort. You'll become better and better at it over time and you'll have some great conversations along the way.

Star**Gazer**

Learn 10 constellations

The Star Gazer Challenge invites you to learn to recognize 10 constellations in the next 30 days. Most likely you'll be able to learn the names and locations in a single evening. Get a book or app that identifies constellations, pick a clear night, and invite one or more friends over to learn the constellations together. It will be like playing a game or solving a puzzle—and will be much more fun when you do it with someone else. You could even prepare some food to eat together and make an entire evening of it.

When was the last time you slowed down and gazed at the stars? So often we don't even notice the beautiful world that we live in and don't pause to look and take in its majesty. Taking time to observe the stars is especially powerful as it puts our lives into perspective. Engaging your brain to learn something new is great too! Once you know more about the constellations, you'll be more likely to take a moment and identify them when you're out at night—hopefully bringing to memory the experience you had with your friends learning together.

Story**Book**

Write down 5 stories

Emotional

Occupational

The Story Book Challenge invites you to write down five stories that you have shared in the past to get your point across or could use in the future to help explain a point you're trying to make. Think of stories that you have referred to time and again in your life and write five of them down. Don't worry about the quality of your writing. You will never read the stories verbatim, but writing them down will help you remember them better for when you need to give a talk or simply make a point. You may even consider putting the point of the story at the top as the topic, so it's easier to locate the story you need later on.

We think data and reasoning are the best ways to convince others of our position, but it's not necessarily so. Emotional appeal can be a much more effective way to win the hearts and support of others. Hearing a story can transform the opinions of a listener in an effortless and enjoyable way. The hope of this challenge is that it will inspire you to build a library of your stories to which you will add over the course of your life. Each time you tell a new story or one you haven't written down yet, add it to your library. Besides being useful to you, your stories can also serve as a memoir for your loved ones.

CHALLENGE
94

Take**Charge**

Lead an initiative

Social

Occupational

The Take Charge Challenge invites you to proactively find a way to lead a new initiative. This could be an initiative at work, at home, with your friends, in the neighborhood, at church, or any other organization. Look for something that needs to be done and volunteer to lead the effort. It should be something that requires the involvement of others to accomplish—the idea is to lead the people helping you, not do everything yourself. Pick something you believe in—it will make the experience easier and more satisfying.

On the surface, leadership may look like a way to get recognition and power, but true leadership is quite the opposite—it is motivating and inspiring others to work towards a common goal. It can be hard to build a united vision and then get everyone to execute on it. It takes patience and understanding and the ability to work with different personality types. Leading others can be frustrating and a heavy burden to carry, but in the end it will make you a better person and ultimately a better follower when it's someone else's turn to lead. What will you help others accomplish—and what will you learn along the way?

Word**Wise**

Learn a new word daily

The Word Wise Challenge invites you to learn a new word every day for the next 30 days. Subscribe to a word website, download an app, or compile your own list. With almost half a million entries in the *Merriam-Webster Unabridged Dictionary*, there are plenty of words to choose from, especially as the average adult only knows 20,000–35,000 words. Each day, select a word and read its definition. To reinforce your learning, consider searching the Internet to find ways the word is used in a sentence. The context will help you better remember the word.

Remember when you were in school and used to get a new, weekly spelling/vocabulary list to memorize? Well, there are still more words to learn and memorizing words is still good for you. Your brain is like a muscle and memorizing is a great exercise for it. It's amazing how a new word you learned starts to magically appear in your life. What unknown words go past you today? Imagine how the fidelity of your life will increase as you expand your vocabulary!

Physical

Occupational

Garage Sale

Sell a used item

Social

Financial

The Garage Sale Challenge invites you to sell something you no longer need. No, you can't just give it away, you need to sell it for money. Go big and have a traditional garage sale or use an online service and list a single item. You could even keep it simple and offer to sell something to a friend that you know he or she would enjoy. Sell a used video game or some old sports equipment to a resale store. See what you can get for that unwanted jewelry at a pawnshop. Perhaps there's good money in an old baseball card or a coin collection.

Selling something you no longer need can be a great way to get a little extra money and declutter your life at the same time. The process of selecting one or more things to sell can also help you make better purchases in the future—helping you understand what types of things give you the most satisfaction and are the most enduring. Also, if you're clearing closet space, you may want to keep it uncluttered by not buying more. If you don't need the money, think of those who will benefit from getting some good stuff at a really great price. However you look at it, selling unneeded items can be a great experience!

Great**Deal**

Comparison shop

SALE 50% OFF

The Great Deal Challenge invites you to try to comparison shop for five things you buy in the next 30 days. This is easy for online purchases, but can be more challenging for purchases you make in a store. Sure you could look up prices online while you're at a store, but it may actually pay to visit another store since some specials are unadvertised and can only be found physically in the store. Many stores price match, so even if one store has a higher price, you can get a lower price by showing proof (a newspaper ad or webpage) of the lower price at a competitor. If you forget to check a second source before you buy, check it out afterward to see if you could have saved any money.

In today's busy world, comparison shopping may seem like something you don't have time for, but the extra time it takes may be just what you need. Comparison shopping slows the buying process down, helping you cut down on impulse buying. By the time you consider all the options, you may find that you don't really need what you wanted to buy after all. If you do end up purchasing the item, you'll have peace of mind that you got the best price available. How much money do you think you will save in the next 30 days?

Grocery Bill

Minimize spending on food

Physical

Financial

The Grocery Bill Challenge invites you to minimize the amount of money you spend on food over the next 30 days—which means you'll need to track every dollar you spend on food. Of course, you still need to eat and you'll continue to buy food throughout the month, but you can achieve dramatic savings if you use coupons and focus on how and where you buy your food. Making a meal at home typically costs much less than going out. Likewise, bringing your lunch to work can be much more economical than buying it. Even when you are eating in, there can be dramatic differences in cost, depending on what you choose to eat and how much you eat.

If you do go out to eat, eating at a counter-order restaurant usually costs less since you don't have to tip a server. Ordering water to drink can save you money, and a few calories too! Try splitting a meal as an option. You can still eat tasty and healthy foods without spending a lot. Food is typically one of the largest areas of discretionary spending. With a little effort, you'll be surprised at how much money you can save in 30 days. Track what you spend to eat and see how it changes your eating, dining, and shopping habits. What will you do with the money you save?

Money**Smart**

Read a financial book

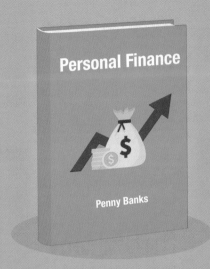

Purpose

Emotional

The Money Smart Challenge invites you to read a financial self-help book. Check out the best-seller list, ask a friend for ideas, or find an online article that recommends books in this category. See what books your local library has available—most have digital books as well. Consider reading the book with your partner so you're both on board with any changes you may need to make to your spending habits. If reading is not your thing, get an audio book and listen to it while you exercise or commute to work. Reading a financial self-help book may be grueling for you, like a hard workout, but some authors find a way to make it an interesting read, and it will be worth it.

Being financially healthy is a lot like being physically healthy. It takes a lifetime to build good habits. Also, depending on your phase of life, your habits will need to change. Plus, there's always room for improvement. It's true that money will not make you happy, but not having enough money can certainly limit your options in life and can make things more difficult. Take this chance to sharpen your financial skills. Even if the book only gets you to change a tiny habit, the returns can be significant over a lifetime!

Financial

Net**Worth**

Calculate your net worth

The Net Worth Challenge invites you to calculate your net worth. You've heard about the net worth of movie stars, sports figures, or other famous wealthy people. Have you ever wondered what *your* net worth is? You can calculate it by adding all your assets (what you own) and subtracting all your liabilities (what you owe). Use an online tool or simply calculate it by hand. Assets include: bank accounts, investment accounts, cars, properties, businesses, and personal property. Liabilities include: loans (car, home, student, etc.) and credit card balances.

Of course, your true worth has nothing to do with money, but knowing your net worth is a great way to understand your financial health. By tracking it over time, you'll be able to see your financial progress and set new financial goals. You might think you are doing well if your income is growing, but if your net worth is flat or declining, it is a signal that you need to manage your finances better. Seeing your net worth puts your assets and debts in perspective. It may be considered ideal to have no debt, but if your assets outweigh your debts, you may be doing just fine. Also, lenders may use net worth to determine whether you qualify for a loan or not. Find out your net worth!

Financial

Night In
Invite some friends over

The Night In Challenge invites you to have some friends over to your place. Have dinner together, enjoy dessert, play games, watch a movie or sporting event, sit around and talk, or some combination of these. If you do decide to serve food, make it yourself—or ask your friends to bring some. Part of this challenge is to have a good time together by staying in and not spending too much. Keep the food simple and, remember, some of the most satisfying comfort food is very basic. No need to buy a movie or a new game; simply watch one you already own or play one that you or your friends already have. It will be just as fun!

When we want to connect with our friends, it's so easy to go out together—but that can get expensive, and it's not necessarily more satisfying or fun. In many ways, spending time together at your home can be a richer experience. Your home is part of who you are, and so is the food you prepare and the plates you serve it on. Sure you'll have to clean your house to get ready, but that's a great motivation to spruce things up and maybe even get a few repairs done! Accept your friends' offer to help you clean up after dinner so you aren't left with a big mess after they leave. Who will you invite over?

Time**Saver**

Shop for groceries online

The Time Saver Challenge invites you to order your groceries online for the next 30 days. You can either have them delivered to your home or pick them up at the store, whatever is most economical and convenient for you. Shop around for the best deal. Some grocery stores provide this service for free or a very small fee. Be sure to order your groceries online the same way at least twice so you can experience how easy it can be to reorder the same things from your first shopping list.

If you've never ordered groceries online before, you may be concerned about higher prices or about not being able to pick out your own produce. As far as produce goes, watch for the specials and they will generally lead you to what's in season. As for the cost, even if the prices are a little higher and you miss a few specials, you will most likely end up spending less when you shop online because it forces you to plan out what you really need and avoid impulse buying. Give it a try. You may like it and decide to do it again. Think of what you'll do with the time that you save!

Financial

TreasureHunt

Buy a used item

The Treasure Hunt Challenge invites you to buy something that is used. Pick a Saturday to go check out garage sales. Visit a thrift store. Consider buying a refurbished phone, computer, or other technology. Search through online ads or virtual garage sales to see if you can find something you need. Buy a used video game. Walk through a used book store. Browse a sporting goods store that has used equipment. If you're handy, you may even find something for free that you could easily repair—like an old lawnmower or a vacuum.

It's easy to get in the habit of buying new because it's faster and easier to find what you're looking for. There's also the pleasure of having something new that no one has touched before; but does it really matter if someone has used something before? What you buy becomes "used" the minute you take it out of the package. Also, it saves waste to buy something that someone has already used. You can also save a significant amount of money when you purchase used items. You just need to be willing to do some searching. You can often find a higher-quality used item for less than a new standard item would cost. So, get ready for an adventure and see what treasures you can find!

Financial

CHALLENGE
104

WaterPlease

No drinks when you eat out

Physical

The Water Please Challenge invites you to pass on drinks whenever you eat out for the next 30 days. What if you had a coupon for 30% off at every restaurant you go to? You do! By choosing water instead of soda or alcohol when dining out, you can reduce your average check by 30%—a nice chunk of savings. You'd certainly save more if you didn't dine out at all, but maybe that doesn't work with your lifestyle or isn't what you desire. Dining with only water allows you to still eat at the same restaurants, just as often, but spend much less. Eventually asking for water with your meal will become a habit you won't even have to think about.

The great thing about this challenge is that the benefits aren't just monetary. Soda and alcohol may taste great, but they're not great for you. They contain high amounts of calories with little to no nutritional value, and they're so enjoyable that it's easy to ingest hundreds of empty liquid calories in a single meal. What's more, sugar and alcohol make your organs work harder, which may eventually lead to diabetes or liver failure. So give your wallet a rest and your body a break— ask for water the next time you go out!

Financial